Giammateo Asola:
# Sixteen Liturgical Works

Recent Researches in the Music of the Renaissance is one of a library of four quarterly series making available, for study and performance, early music brought to light in the course of current independent musicological research.

Each volume is devoted to the works of a single composer (or, occasionally, of a single school of composition), selected and prepared for publication largely according to the discretion of the editor.

As a rule, reprints of the separate works in each volume of the series will be made available to performers as soon as possible after the volume is published.

Correspondence should be addressed:

A-R Editions, Inc.
53 Livingston Street
New Haven, Connecticut

Giammateo Asola

# Sixteen Liturgical Works

Edited by Donald M. Fouse

1964
A-R Editions, Inc.
New Haven

# Contents

# Preface

## The Composer and His Works

That Giammateo Asola was a prolific composer of sacred music is attested by his output of approximately forty Masses, well over fifty motets, at least sixty-one Latin hymns, large numbers of vesper psalms, cantilenas, *falsibordoni,* introits, alleluias, Lamentations, *laudes,* and passions, and much other music for the offices.[1] Yet today Asola is known chiefly as a pioneer in the use of *basso continuo,* and only to a lesser extent as a composer of sacred music.[2]

The widespread opinion that Asola was among the earliest composers to use *basso continuo* for organ was first put forth by Otto Kinkeldey.[3] I have tried to discover the basis of his belief but I have had small success: from the entire corpus of Asola's extant works, I have been able to extract only two fragments that have any possible bearing on the matter. The first is the sole remnant of a collection by Asola entitled *Organicus hymnodiae vespertinae,* which contained works for eight voices and was printed in Venice in 1602 by Amadinus. A single part from this collection, not identified by voice, survives among the holdings of the Bayerische Staatsbibliothek in Munich; the part is very likely for organ, but it includes no figuration and is probably merely a doubling of one of the bass parts in the choral score. A second bit of evidence is preserved at the Nationalbibliothek in Vienna — a cantus part to Asola's *Hymnodia vespertina in maioribus anni solemnitatibus,* another lost collection of works for eight voices, printed in Venice by Amadinus in 1602. The part bears the curious subtitle *Organico etiam modulatui accomodata.* Eitner asserted[4] that in a copy of the same collection in Berlin a part for *basso continuo* was included with the cantus part; the Berlin collection, however, has been lost since World War II. Because I have not been able to find all the parts to the *Organicus hymnodiae vespertinae* mentioned by Kinkeldey, I am inclined to believe that he based his judgment on the unidentified part from that collection now at the Bayerische Staatsbibliothek, or on the now-missing Berlin copy of the *Hymnodiae* mentioned by Eitner.

Since no conclusive evidence has so far been presented to show that Asola wrote an independent *basso continuo* part, it is apparent that what fame he now enjoys rests on a doubtful assertion. My opinion is that his true value as a composer of sacred music has been neglected in the meanwhile, and I hope that this small collection will help encourage greater appreciation of his work.

Giammateo Asola, known variously as Giovanni or Joannis, Matteo, Matheo, Maltheo, Matthei, or Matheai Asola, Asula, Asulae, or Asulum, was born in Verona in 1524, according to Francesco Caffi and Giovanni d'Alessi.[5] The date seems doubtful; in the light of other dates given by these authors it implies that Asola did not leave the Collegio of the *Canonici regolari* until he was 45 years old, that he had his first collection published when he was 46, and that he died when he was 85. It does seem more probable that he left the Collegio when he was around 20 years old and died at about the age of 65. The date of his birth, given the plausibility of these assumptions, would be close to 1540.[6]

Asola was apparently destined from the beginning to become a man of the Church. He was educated at the Collegio of the *Canonici regolari,* situated on San Giorgio in Alga, a small island near Venice; the date of his entry into the monastery has not been established. Asola was fortunate in being located there, for in the Venetian monasteries the arts and sciences were cultivated assiduously, and particular emphasis was given to music. During Asola's education the composer Anselmo Negri must have taught at the Collegio, and probably added inspiration to Asola's study of music, for Asola refers to Negri and his position in a letter of dedication appearing in a collection of Asola's Lamentations.[7]

Asola apparently did not leave the Collegio until 1569.[8] From this time until 1577 he lived in Venice where, it may be presumed, he became acquainted with the works of Willaert and the theories of Andrea Gabrieli and Gioseffo Zarlino.[9] During his residence in Venice — and probably for some time before he left the brotherhood — he was composing extensively; two collections of his Masses were published by Gardano in Venice in 1570. During this period of his life, Asola produced one of his few collections of secular music, a series of madrigal settings *a3* of Petrarch's *Vergine*. The set was published by Gardano, and its popularity is indicated by the fact that it went through at least seven separate printings and led eventually to a second volume of madrigals. In Venice Asola also composed a *Completorium per totum annum* (1573), *falsibordoni* (1575), a collection of ten Masses *a4* (1574), a separate Requiem (1576), and two collections of vesper-psalm settings, one *a6* (1576) and the other *a8* (1574).

On the 26th of November, 1577, the Duomo of Treviso appointed Asola *maestro di cappella*, but after a year at Treviso he accepted a better position at the Cappella in Vicenza, where he remained until 1588. Most of his compositions were probably written at Vicenza, including the bulk of his approximately forty Masses. In 1588, leaving as his successor Leone Leoni, his erstwhile pupil, he returned to Venice[10] and was appointed to one of four chaplainships at San Severo, a church under the jurisdiction of the monks of San Lorenzo. Asola had moved into illustrious company; among the composers in Venice at that time were Gioseffo Zarlino, Baldassare Donati, and Giovanni della Croce, all of whom were later masters of the Ducal Chapel. One of the noteworthy products of Asola's career in Venice was a dedication to Palestrina which he wrote for a collection of *Psalmodia vespertina*,[11] including works by himself, Croce, Gastoldi, Leoni, and Porta. The collection was an act of homage; Asola's dedication, *Ad Celeberrimum Coryphaeum D. Jo. Petrum Aloysium Praenestinum,* states with enthusiasm and reverence that Palestrina is the greatest musician of the era.

Asola remained at San Severo until his death, still composing new music for the Church. He died October 1, 1609, after an illness lasting twelve days, and his remains were taken to the church of San Lorenzo, where one of his Requiem Masses was performed at his funeral.

Asola's most notable pupils were Leone Leoni and D. Amedeo Freddi. Leoni succeeded his maestro at Vicenza and stayed there well into the early seventeenth century. Leoni is remembered for his large output of motets and for a *Cantici sacri*, published in 1608. D. Amedeo Freddi was *maestro di cappella* at Vicenza from 1627 until 1634, when he went to the Cappella of the Duomo of Padua. He remained at Padua until his death ten years later.

Whether Asola studied with Vincenzo Ruffo, as stated by Gustave Reese,[12] is open to question. Both composers were born in Verona on uncertain dates, but their paths seem to have crossed infrequently. It is possible that Asola studied with Ruffo before Asola went to the Collegio, for Ruffo taught at the Accademia Filarmonica in Verona from 1551 to 1552 and at the cathedral there, as *maestro di cappella,* in 1554. But Ruffo went to Milan in 1574, and in 1580 to Sacile, near Treviso, where he died in 1587.[13] Since Asola was at Treviso only from 1577 to 1578 it seems unlikely that the two composers came into contact with one another.

Because of the brevity of this collection and the scarcity of published critical material dealing with Asola's music, the introduction here of a few brief generalizations about his style may serve to put the works in this volume into their proper context. A detailed analysis of Asola's works in various forms can be found in my *The Sacred Music of Giammateo Asola.*[14]

That Asola has customarily been included

among the earliest composers to use *basso continuo* may lead one to think that his later years were spent in the service of the young baroque. An examination of his work, however, will reveal that he was consistently faithful to the characteristic usages of the late Renaissance as exemplified especially in the late compositions of Palestrina. His music represents stylistically the last stage in the systematization of dissonance as well as the familiar late-sixteenth century relationship between time value and rhythmic context. Block chordal style and imitative settings with canon are present in the works of Asola, but most of his music is in a free, imitative contrapuntal style balanced occasionally with brief sections of free, non-imitative counterpoint. Some of the less spectacular innovations of the Venetian school, particularly in the treatment of *cori spezzati,* can be found in Asola's *a8* works and to a lesser extent in his *a6* works.

The organizing principle of Asola's style, as of Palestrina's, is the invention and combination of melodic lines. The internal rhythmic structure of his works, generally speaking, is such that note values are longer at the beginnings of phrases, gradually become shorter and rhythmically more complex, then expand again at the cadences. Paired imitation is infrequent. Musical rhyme is present in the hymns and usually absent from the other sacred works, although certain cadential formulae, which tend to strengthen the formal coherence produced by recurring motives, appear frequently in all his music. Asola is markedly conservative in the use of the ecclesiastical modes, and in all essential respects his modal writing is similar to Palestrina's. Dissonance and suspension in Asola's music are treated, for the most part, in the usual fashion of the late Renaissance.

Asola's motet (the first musical form represented in this collection) is generally rather brief and in an imitative contrapuntal style. His musical treatment of motet texts is characteristic of the form, in that each line or division has its independent theme, generally imitated in all voices before the next line of text is introduced. The motets are most frequently based on antiphons, which they paraphase quite freely. Usually the chant melody appears most completely in the cantus, but it may be divided among several voices. The chant melody is generally fragmented, with freely composed sections interposed between sections based on the *cantus firmus.* Free, imitative counterpoint alternates with non-imitative counterpoint for the most part, and only occasionally with sections in chordal style.

Asola's hymn settings (three of which follow the motets in this collection) are stylistically like his motets. Melodic treatment of the *cantus firmus* varies from strict long-note settings to very free settings of the chant melody, but the usual treatment is moderate, freer than the long-note extreme and stricter than in the motets. Often one melody is used for more than one hymn (an example is the melody of *Deus tuorum militum,* included in this collection; the melody can be found in three other hymns by Asola, in a total of nine settings), but no two settings of the same melody are ever alike. Asola usually sets the even-numbered verses of his hymns, a practice in which he is at variance with Palestrina, whose settings are generally of odd-numbered verses.

Asola's settings of the complete vesper psalms survive in greater abundance than his works in any other form except, perhaps, the Mass. Most of his vesper psalms follow the usual Renaissance plan: the incipits are intoned—most often by the tenor, less frequently by the bassus — and the remainder of the psalm is set in a simple harmonic fashion similar to *falsobordone* style. A number of exceptions to the unadorned harmonic style of his vesper psalms do occur, however, and two such exceptions are included in this collection. The *a5 Magnificat, Primi toni,* is very similar stylistically to Asola's *a5* Masses, particularly his settings of the *Crucifixus;* all five voices are equally and independently treated in a throughgoing imitative fashion. The *a6* psalm setting *Beatus vir* is in a *cori spezzati* style found only in Asola's *a6* and *a8* settings. Asola's interest in this and similar works is with combinations of voices or timbres; the feature is unique in the *a6* settings, which are for undivided choir — Asola's *a8* settings are clearly for divided choir and are treated so. In the *a6* settings combinations of two or three voices alternate with sections in full *a6* block-chordal style, the latter often occurring when a climax is desired, in direct contrast with devices used for climatic effects in the *Magnificat* mentioned above.

Asola's *Sacrae laudes*, two of which appear in this volume, are well-composed, contrapuntal, imitative *a3* motets, generally very similar in style to the *a4* motets, and should not be confused with the once-popular *laude* in *falsobordone* style.

## The Edition

Two considerations were served in the selection of works for this publication: I chose music that (a) is likely to appeal to scholars and performers interested in Renaissance music, and (b) represents most effectively the mature style of the composer. Works that are of a purely functional nature, completely subordinate to service purposes and not of particular musical interest — settings in *falsobordone* style and simple psalm settings — have not been included. To make the collection as comprehensive as possible, I have tried to supply representative music *a3, a4, a5, a6,* both with and without canon and *cantus firmus* treatment, and otherwise illustrating special features of Asola's art.

Asola's most important sacred works, other than his Masses, are his motets, represented in this collection by nine from a collection of thirty-seven. Second in importance to the motets are Asola's Latin hymns; I have selected three, including eight separate settings, from a collection of forty hymns. The *Magnificat* is a superior *a5* composition, and is taken from a collection of works by various composers dedicated to Palestrina, mentioned in the biography. The *a6* psalm setting *Beatus vir* was selected for, in addition to its general attractiveness, its *cori spezzati* style. To round out

the collection two *a3 Sacrae laudes* were selected because they contain some relatively complex and very interesting writing for a small number of voices.

The following list of works in this volume includes the collections from which the works were taken and, in parentheses, the library from which my copy of each collection was obtained.

Sacrae cantiones:

> In Nativitate Domini: *Dies sanctificatus*
> In festo S. S. Innocentium: *Cantabant sancti*
> In die Pentecostes: *Dum complerentur*
> In festo Sanctae Trinitatis: *O altitudo*
> In festo Corporis Christi: *O sacrum convivium*
> In festo S. Io. Baptistae: *Inter natos mulierum*
> In Assumptione B. V. Mariae: *Exaltata est sancta Dei Genitrix*
> In festis S. Crucis: *Hoc signum Crucis*
> In festis Apostolorum, et martyrum tempore Pascali: *Filiae Jerusalem*

> All from: *Sacrae cantiones in totius anni solennitatibus paribus quaternis vocibus decantande,* Venezia: Amadino, 1596 (Lucca: Archivo del Seminario).

Hymni ad vespertinas:

> In festo S. Stephanii Prothomartyris: *Deus tuorum militum*
> In Annunciatione et festivitatibus B. V. Mariae: *Ave maris stella*
> In festo plurimorum Martyrum: *Sanctorum meritis*

> All from: *Hymni ad vespertinas omnium solemnitatum horas, quatuor vocibus . . . ,* Venezia: Vincenti et Amadino, 1585 (Ferrara: Biblioteca Comunale), and *Secunda pars Hymnorum vespertinis omnium solennitatum horis deservientium . . . ,* Venezia: Vincenti et Amadino, 1585 (Bologna: Liceo Musicale).

Magnificat:

> From: *Sacra omnium solemnitatum psalmodia vespertina cum cantico B. V. A. diversis in arte musica praestantiss. viris notulis musicis exornato 5 voc. Ad celebr. ae praestantiss . . . D. Jo. Petrum Aloysium Praenestinum,* Venezia: Amadino, 1592 (Bologna: Liceo Musicale).

Beatus vir:

From: *Vespertina majorum solennitatum psalmodia senis vocibus,* Venezia: H. Scotti, 1576 (Bologna: Liceo Musicale).

Sacrae laudes:

*Deus canticum novum*
*Cantate Domino*

From: *Missae due decemque sacrae laudes, 3 vocibus concinendae . . . 2nd impressio,* Venezia: Amadinus, 1588 (Bologna: Liceo Musicale).

I have tried to make the music in this volume useful to both scholars and potential performers without violating the interests of either group — that is, I hope that scholars will be able to glean from my score an accurate idea of the original source, and that performers will be able to see in it a practical transcription which can be used by a choir without very much confusion.

The music originally appeared in the white mensural notation usual in printed editions of its time; I had little difficulty transcribing it. All of the compositions are in *tempus imperfectum, proportio dupla* (¢), reduced by one-half in transcription. In all but one case (*In die Pentecostes,* p. 9, where the second voice is so low as to permit performance only by tenors) I have transcribed the music in a fashion that will at least keep open the possibility of performance by modern "mixed" or "men's" choruses. The original clefs and time signatures are given at the beginning of each work — and, in the hymns, at the beginning of each section.

Ligatures are of common forms — two white semibreves, semibreve followed by a blackened semibreve, semibreve followed by a dotted semibreve, and two semibreves followed by a breve — and cause no problems in transcription. The occurrence of a ligature in the source is indicated in the transcription by a horizontal bracket: ⌐♩ ♩⌐. Coloration is confined to semibreves followed by minims, transcribed as ♩· ♪, and breves followed by semibreves, transcribed as ♩· ♩. An instance of coloration

in the source is shown by a dashed line placed above the bracket indicating a ligature:

⌐---⌐ ♩ ♩· ♪.

Accidentals in the original have been left out of the edition where they repeat within the bars supplied by the editor.

The problem of *musica ficta* loomed unexpectedly large in the preparation of this edition because of a rather inconsistent use of accidentals on the part of Asola and his printers. So far as possible, I have inserted editorial accidentals according to the customary reckoning, bearing in mind the necessity that they be consistent with the accidentals in the source. I have not inserted accidentals that I consider "conjectural", but the reader (or the conductor) should, of course, freely omit or add editorial accidentals at his discretion. In this edition, editorial accidentals have been removed from their usual location above the note and placed in brackets *before* the note, for the benefit of singers and sightreaders.

In general, the texts were laid out with more than usual care in printed editions of Asola's music — that is, inconsistency in the relation of textual phrase to musical line is rare. The spelling and punctuation of the texts, however, is far from helpful to the present-day editor. In this edition none of the occasionally archaic wording of the texts has been altered, but punctuation and hyphenation have been regularized and spelling has been changed, where necessary, to conform with current ecclesiastical usage. Text supplied by the editor, where the repetition of a passage is indicated by the abbreviation *ij,* has been given in italics. Performers, I believe, should feel free to redistribute the texts of the works as they see fit; in some cases the present distribution is, to say the least, improbable.

In all but two cases Asola's titles for the works in this volume have been preserved in their original wording and spelling. In each of the three hymns (*In festo S. Stephanii Prothomartyris, In Annunciatione et festivitatibus B. V. Mariae, In festo plurimorum Martyrum*) I have bracketed the subtitles of the odd-numbered stanzas and provided subtitles for the even-numbered stanzas, for the sake of clarity and consistent usage. I have also provided the titles of the two *Sacrae laudes* (*Deus canticum novum, Cantate Domino*).

The very few specific instances in which this edition deviates from the sources are as follows:

*Page 22, measure 47, cantus*: The final eighth note is d′ in the original, an obvious misprint; it has been changed to c′ in this edition.

*Page 47 measure 1*: In the source, the specification "Quinque vocibus" appears at the beginning of the cantus part; the second voice is the editor's realization of the canon.

*Page 47, measure 6, tenor*: The two half notes in the edition appear, incorrectly, as a ligature in the source.

*Page 54, measure 1*: In the source, the words "Tribus vocibus" appear at the beginning of the cantus part to this section of the hymn; the words "Monstra te esse tacitum" appear at this point in the bass part to the hymn.

*Page 56, measure 1*: In the source, the words "Cum sex vocibus" appear at the beginning of the cantus part to this section of the hymn; the second voice is the editor's realization of the canon. The fifth voice was originally printed with the bass part.

*Page 78, measure 62, bassus*: The half-note f has been supplied in place of an incorrect d appearing in the source.

*Page 111, measure 45, cantus*: At this point, which begins a new stave in the original, an obviously incorrect alto C clef appears in place of the usual mezzo-soprano C clef.

For furnishing microfilm of Asola's music, and for permitting its study and transcription, I wish to express my gratitude to the Liceo Musicale in Bologna, Italy, the Archivo del Seminario in Lucca, Italy, and the Biblioteca Comunale in Ferrara, Italy.

Donald M. Fouse
Wisconsin State College
Oshkosh, Wisconsin

May, 1964

# Notes

[1] A comprehensive list of Asola's compositions may be found in my *The Sacred Music of Giammateo Asola* (Dissertation, University of North Carolina, 1960), pp. 174-184, obtainable from University Microfilms, Ann Arbor, Michigan (Order No.: Mic. 60-6985).

[2] Gustave Reese, *Music in the Renaissance* (New York: Norton, 1954), p. 426.

[3] Otto Kinkeldey, *Orgel und Klavier in der Musik des 16. Jahrhunderts* (Leipzig: Breitkopf und Haertel, 1910), p. 204.

[4] Robert Eitner, *Biographische-bibliographischer Quellen-Lexikon der Musiker und Musikgelehrten der christlichen Zeitvechnung bis zur Mittedes 19. Jahrhunderts* (Leipzig: Breitkopf und Haertel, 1898).

[5] Francesco Caffi, *Della vita e della opera di Giammateo Asola* (Padua: P. Prosperini, 1862), pp. 1-13; Giovanni d'Alessi, *La cappella musicale del Duomo di Treviso (1300-1633)* (Treviso: Vedelago, 1954), pp. 127-132. Although I have in this instance attempted to discredit the information given by these authors, I have been obliged to rely on them for much of the material that appears in the rest of this brief biography. So far as I am concerned, a definitive treatment of Asola's career has yet to emerge, and I regret that the magnitude of such an undertaking has put it outside the scope of the research attending the preparation of this volume of his music.

[6] Several other dates have been proposed for Asola's birth and have been rejected. They are: 1560 – Carlo Schmidl, *Dizionario universale dei musicisti* (Milan: Sanzogno, 1938), probably the source for Gustave Reese, *Music in the Renaissance*, p. 426; 1550 – *Baker's Biographical Dictionary of Musicians* (New York: Schirmer, 1959); 1542 – Donald M. Fouse, "The Vesper Hymns of

Giammateo Asola" (unpublished Master's thesis, Department of Music, University of North Carolina, 1958), p. 1. If Asola were born in 1560 his first collection of masses (1570) would have been printed when he was ten years old. I know of no foundation for the 1550 date.

[7]*Lamentatione improperia, et aliae sacrae laudes in hebdomada maiori decantandae tribus vocibus* (Venezia: Amadino, 1588).

[8]Caffi, *op.cit.*, p. 6; d'Alessi, *op.cit.*, p. 127.

[9]Caffi, *op.cit.*, p. 6; d'Alessi, *op.cit.*, p. 127. D'Alessi bases his information on Jac. Philippi Tomasini, *Annals Canonicorum Saecularium S.* *Georgii in Alga* (Utini: Schiratti, 1542-     ), p. 536.

[10]Caffi, *op.cit.*, p. 6; d'Alessi, *op.cit.*, pp. 128-129.

[11]*Sacra omnium solemnitatum psalmodia vespertina cum cantico B. V. A. diversis in arte musica praestantiss. viris notulis musicis exornato 5 voc. Ad celebr. ae praestantiss. . . D. Jo. Petrum Aloysium Praenestinum* (Venezia: Amadino, 1592).

[12]Reese, *op.cit.*, p. 493.

[13]*Ibid.*, p. 416.

[14]*Op.cit.*

# Sacrae cantiones
## 1596

# In Nativitate Domini

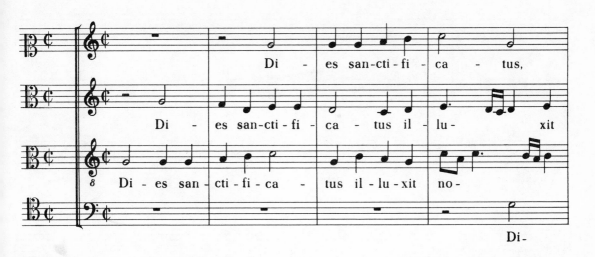

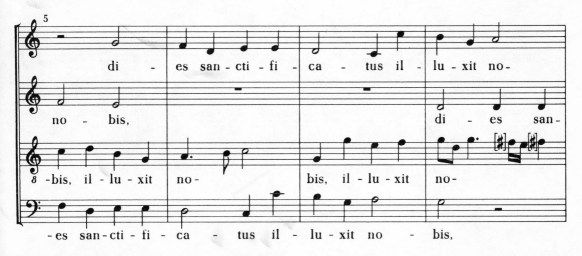

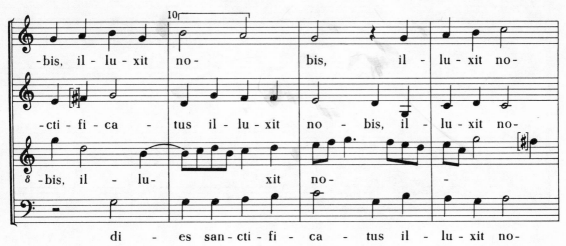

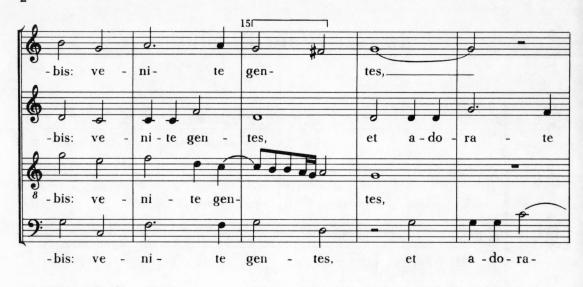

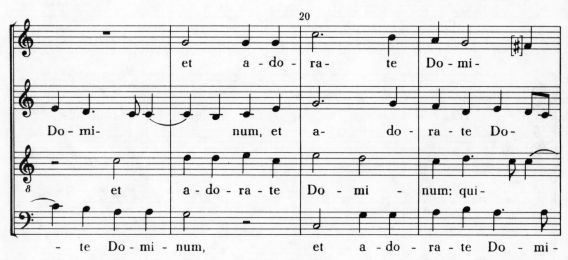

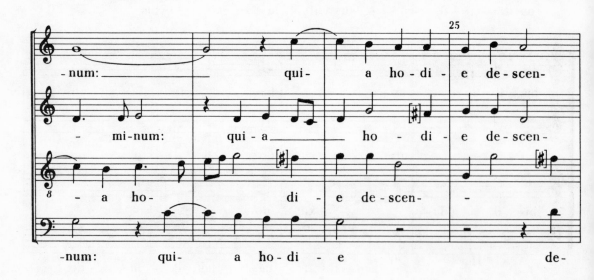

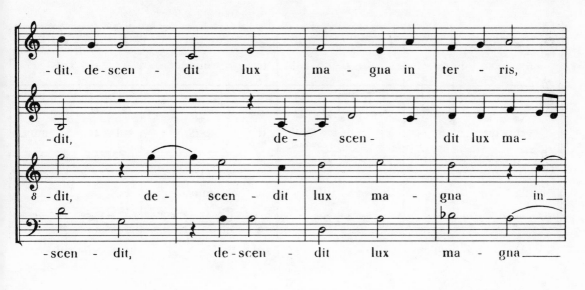

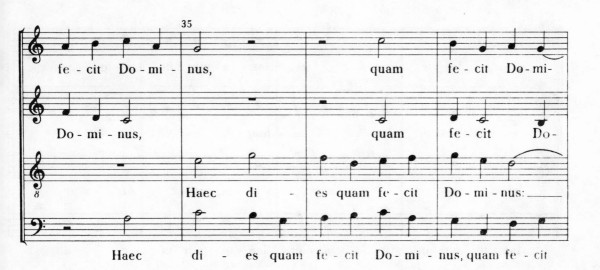

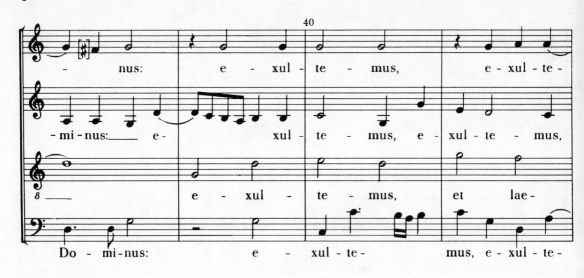

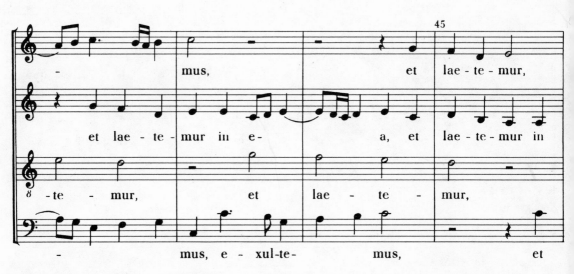

# In festo S.S. Innocentium

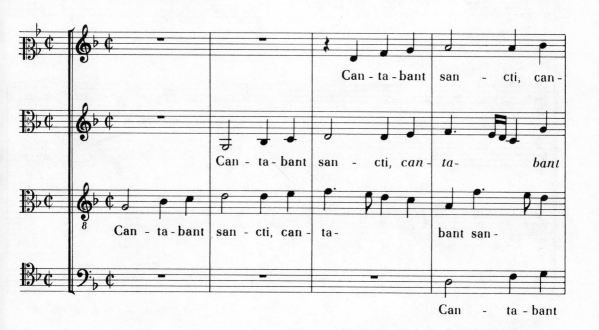

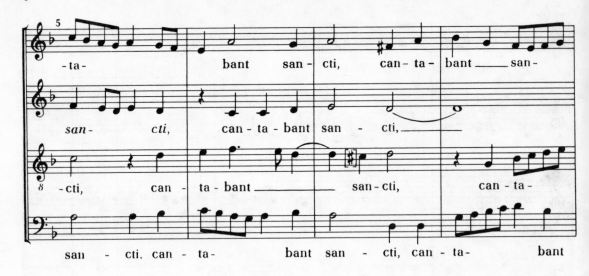

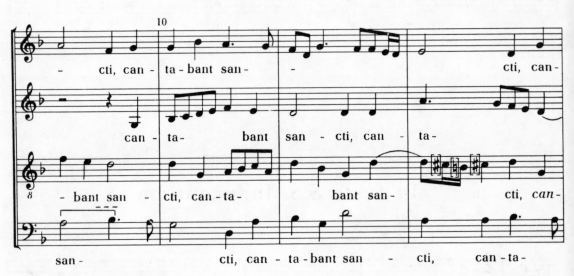

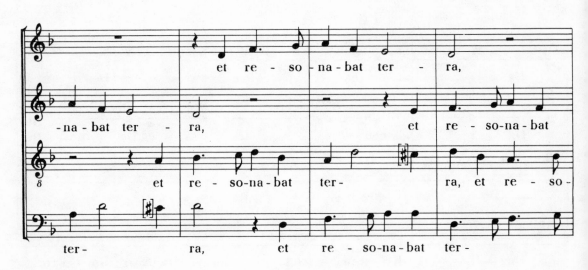

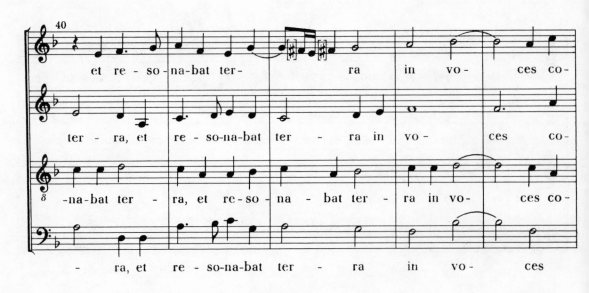

# In die Pentecostes

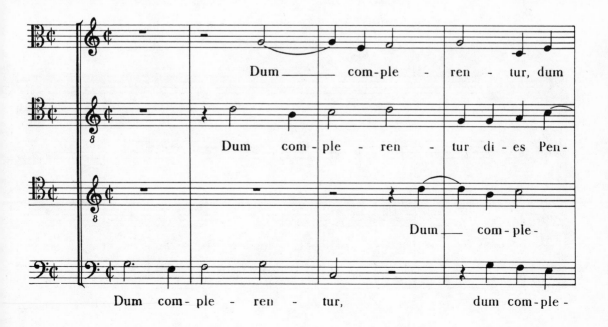

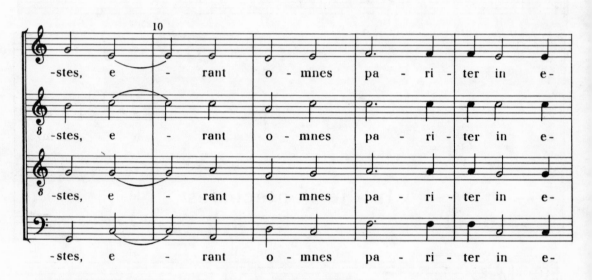

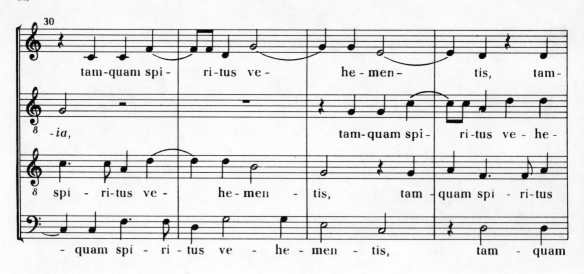

# In festo Sanctae Trinitatis

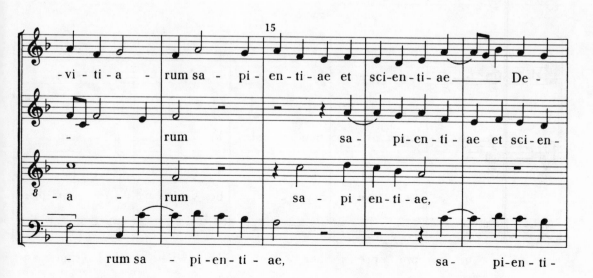

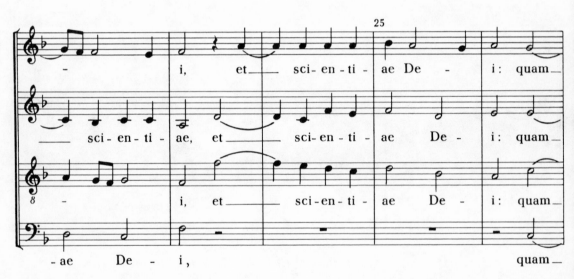

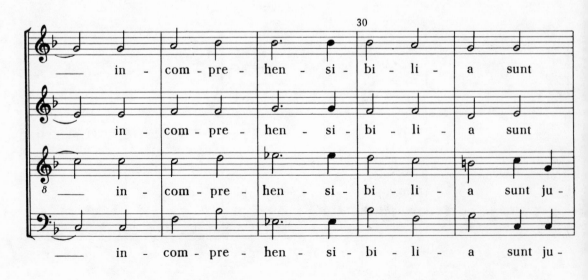

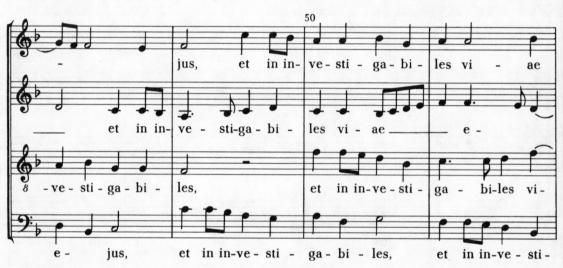

# In festo Corporis Christi

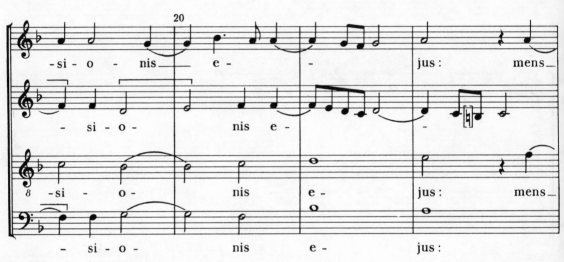

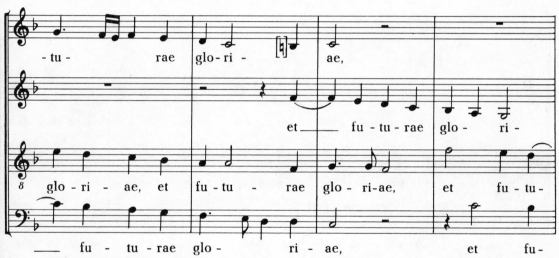

## In festo S. Io. Baptistae

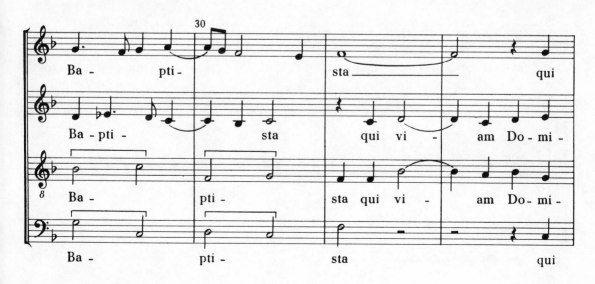

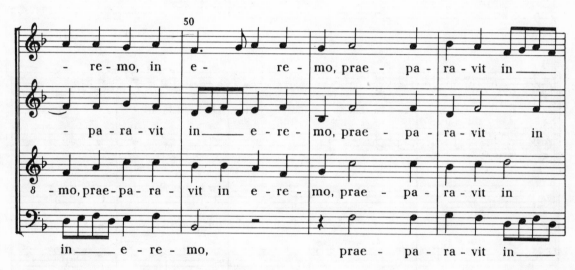

# In Assumptione B.V. Mariae

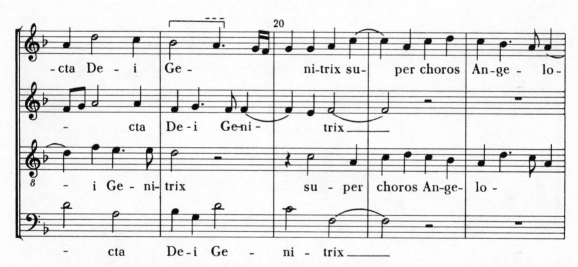

- a re - gna, ad cae-le-sti - a re - gna.

- gna.

ad cae - le - sti-a re - gna.

-gna, ad cae-le - sti-a re - gna.

# In festis S. Crucis

Hoc si - gnum Cru -

Hoc si - gnum Cru -

Hoc si - gnum Cru - cis,

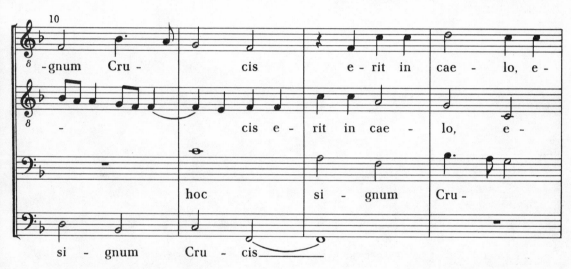

# In festis Apostolorum, et martyrum tempore Pascali

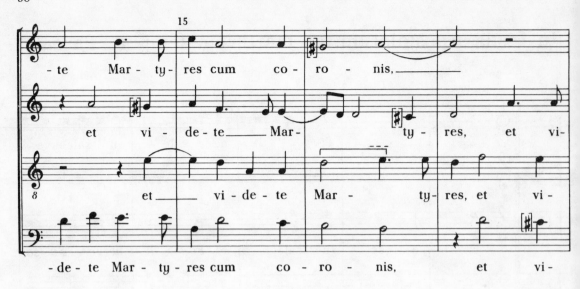

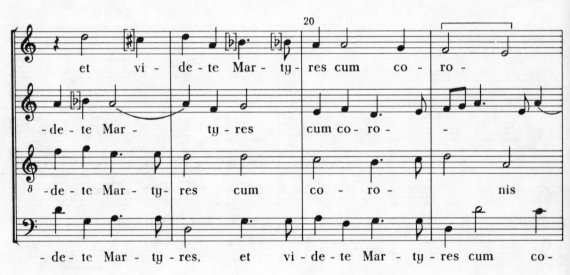

# Hymni ad vespertinas
## 1585

# In festo S. Stephanii Prothomartyris

[1. Deus tuorum militum]
2. Hic nempe mundi gaudia

[3. Poenas cucurrit fortiter]

4. Ob hoc precatu supplici

*Resolutio* may be at upper octave as given or in unison with tenor (not quite as successful).

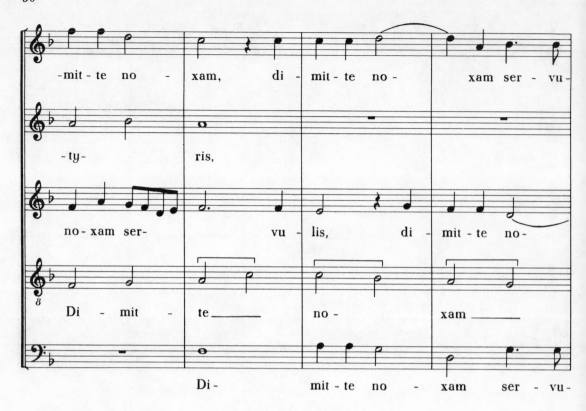

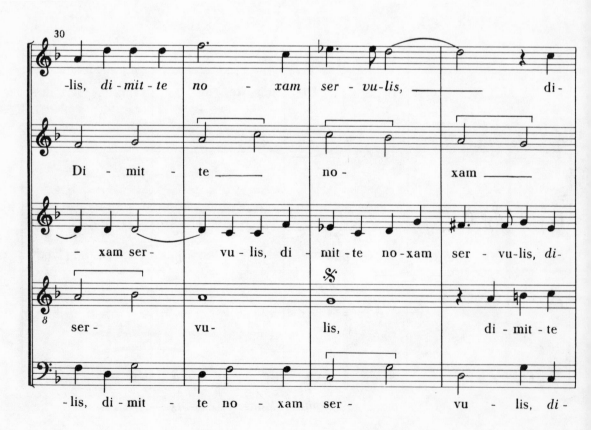

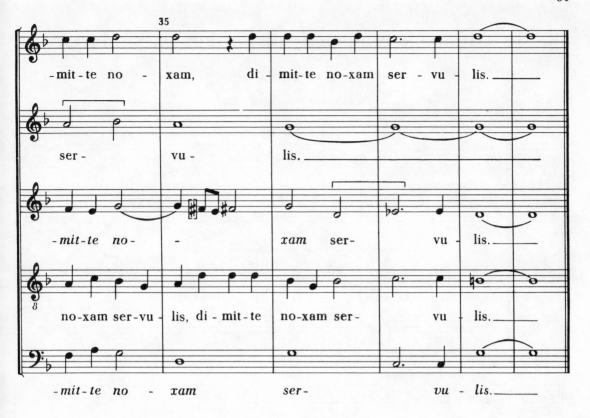

[5. Gloria tibi, Domini]

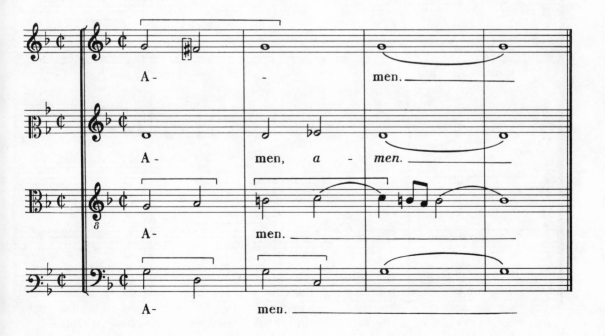

# In Annunciatione et festivitatibus B. V. Mariae

[1. Ave maris stella]

2. Sumens illud Ave

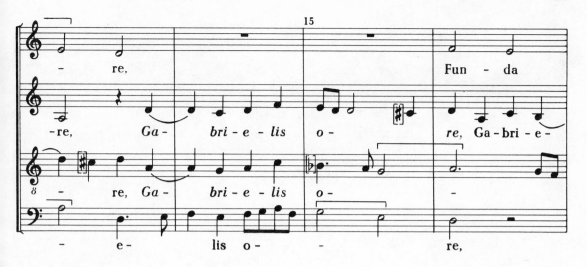

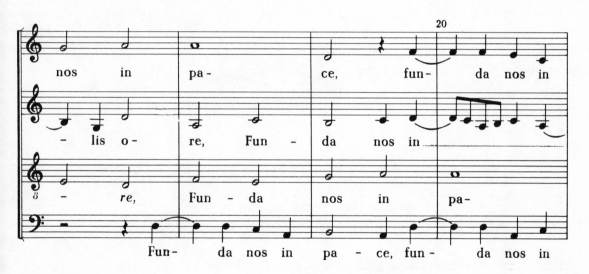

[3. Solve vincla reis]

4. Monstra te esse matrem

## [5. Virgo singularis]
## 6. Vitam praesta puram

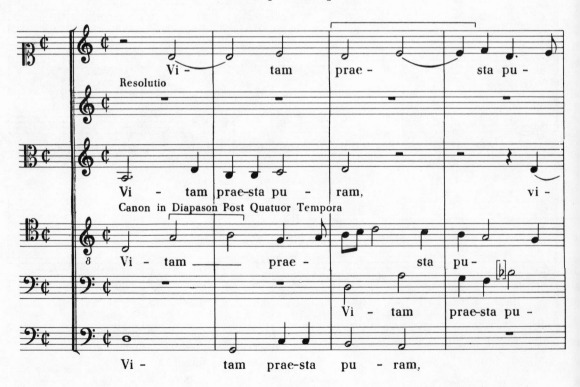

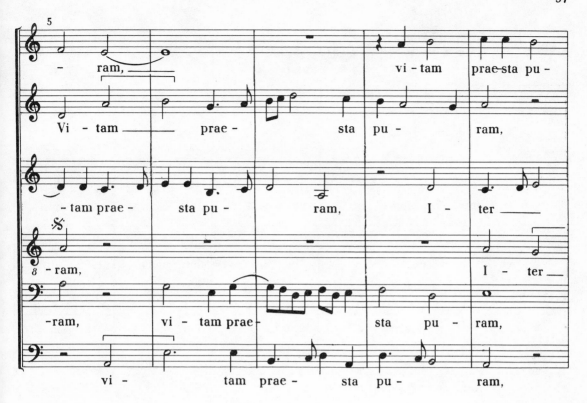

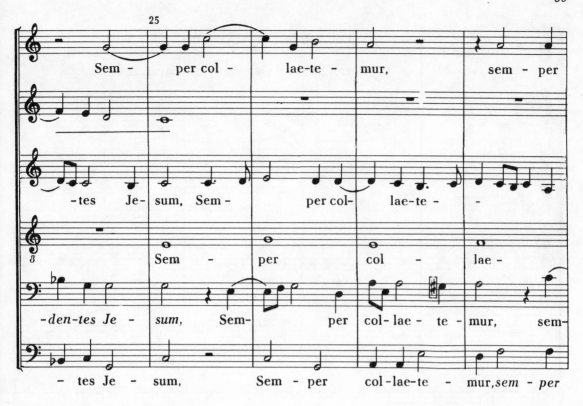

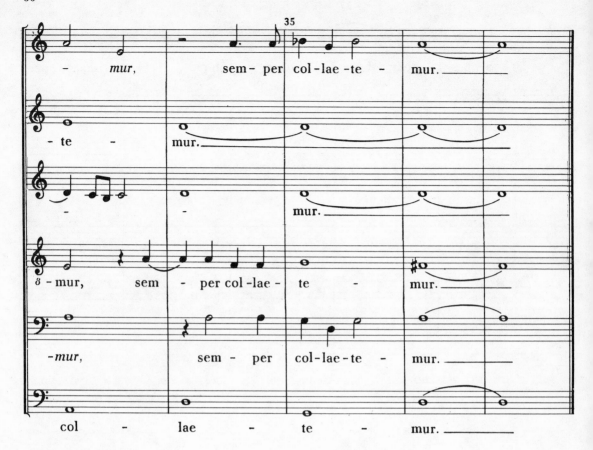

[7. Sit laus Deo Patri]

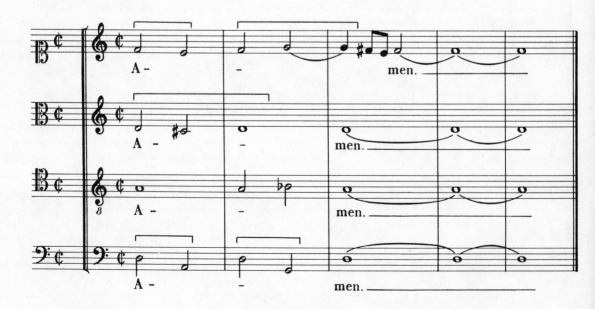

# In festo plurimorum Martyrum

[1. Sanctorum meritis]

2. Hi sunt quos retinens

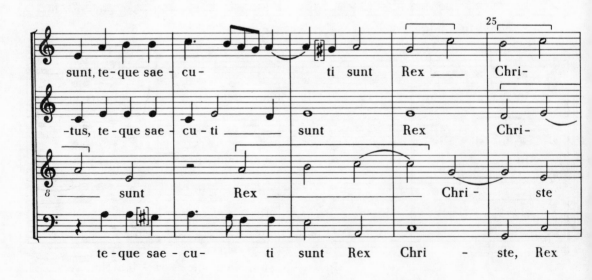

**[3. Hi pro te furias]**

**4. Caeduntur gladiis**

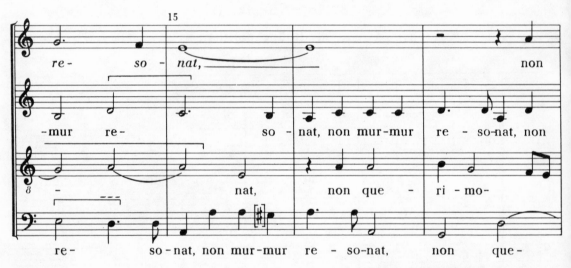

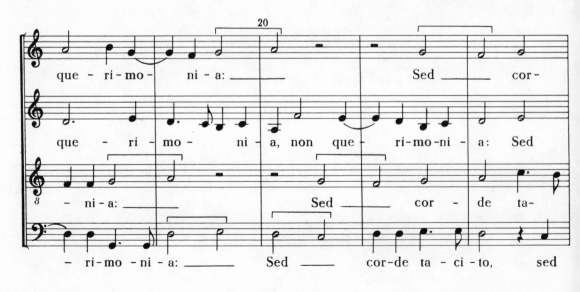

## [5. Quae vox, quae poterit]

## 6. Te summa Deitas

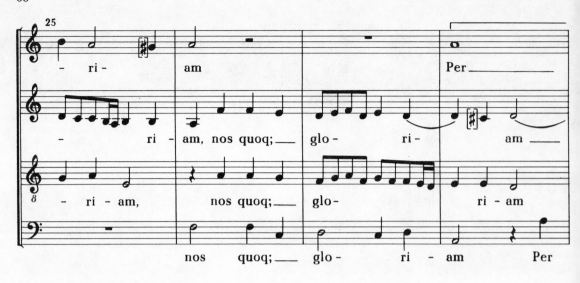

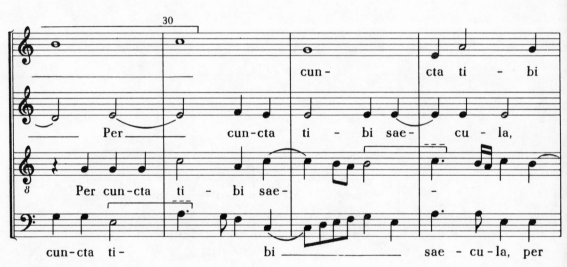

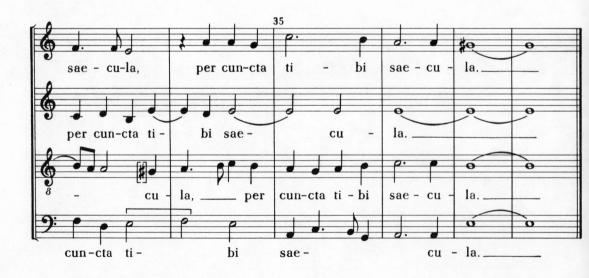

# Magnificat
## 1592

# Magnificat

### Primi toni

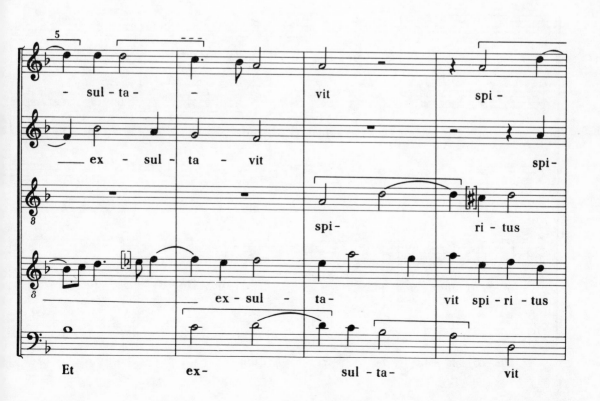

De - o sa - lu - ta - ri me - o.

sa - lu - ta - ri me - o, sa - lu - ta - ri me - o.

in De - o sa - lu - ta - ri me - o.

- ri, sa - lu - ta - ri me - o.

De - o sa - lu - ta - ri me - o.

**4.**

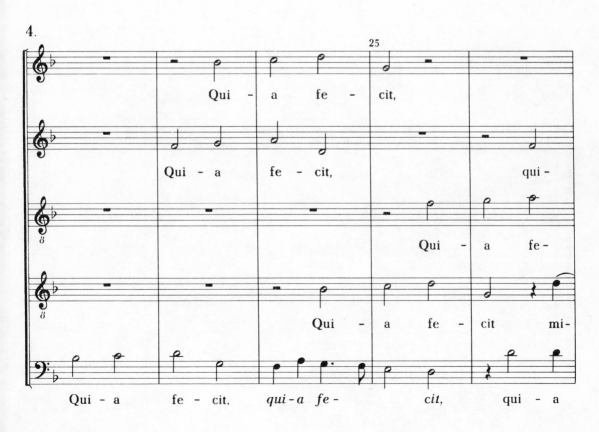

Qui - a fe - cit,

Qui - a fe - cit, qui -

Qui - a fe -

Qui - a fe - cit mi -

Qui - a fe - cit, *qui - a fe - cit,* qui - a

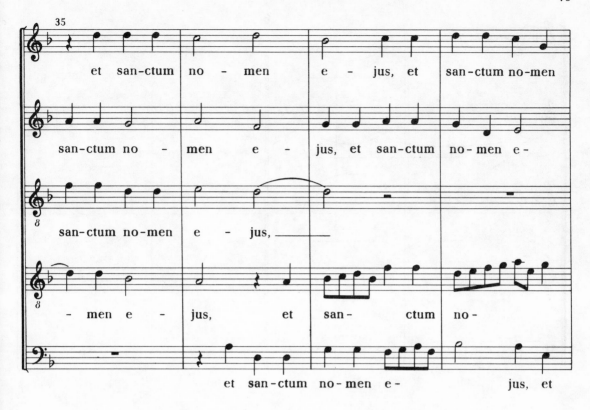

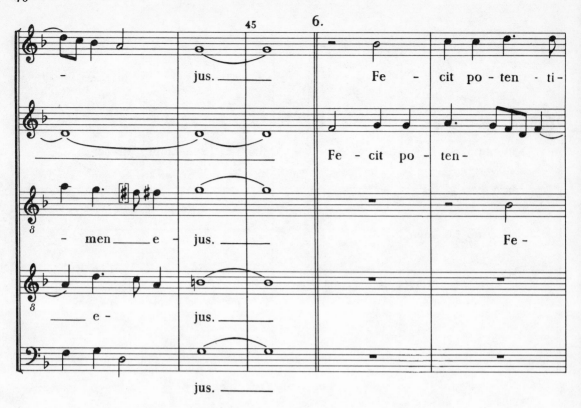

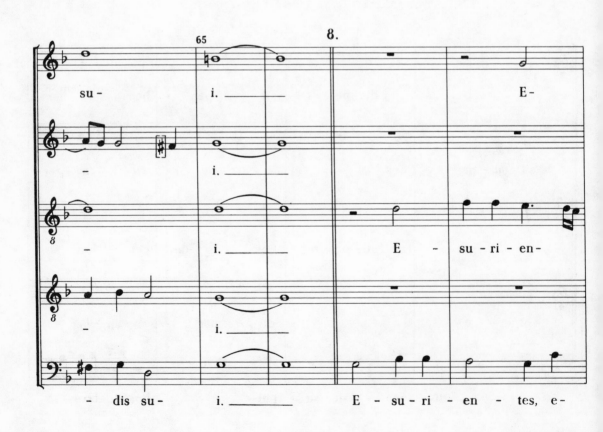

80

-tes, et di - vi - tes di - mi - sit i - na -nes, i-

di - mi - sit i - na - - -

i - na - nes, di - mi - sit i-

-na - - nes, di - mi-

-mi - sit i - na - nes, et di - vi -tes di - mi - sit____

**10.**

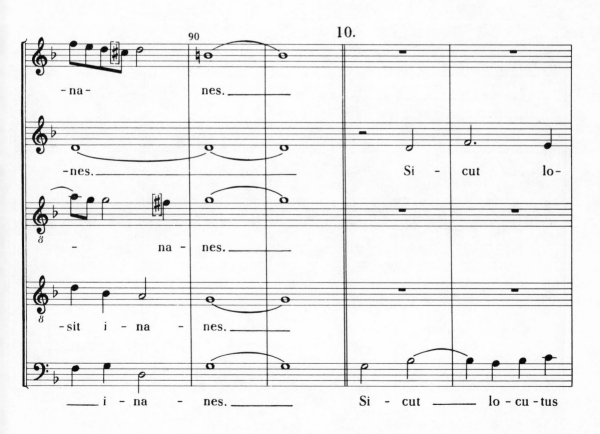

-na - nes._____

-nes.____

- na - nes.____

-sit i - na - nes.____ Si - cut lo-

____ i - na - nes.____ Si - cut ____ lo - cu -tus

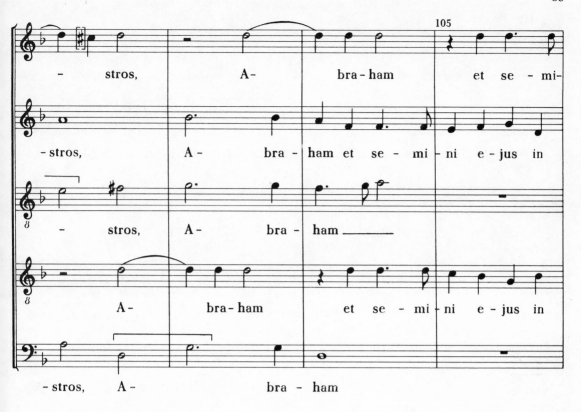

-jus in sae-cu -- la, et se -- mi-ni e -jus in sae - cu-

-jus in sae - cu -- la, et se - mi -ni e -jus in sae-cu-

sae - cu -- la, in sae - cu -

et se - mi-ni e -jus in sae- cu-

-- cu - la, et se-mi- ni e -jus in sae- cu-

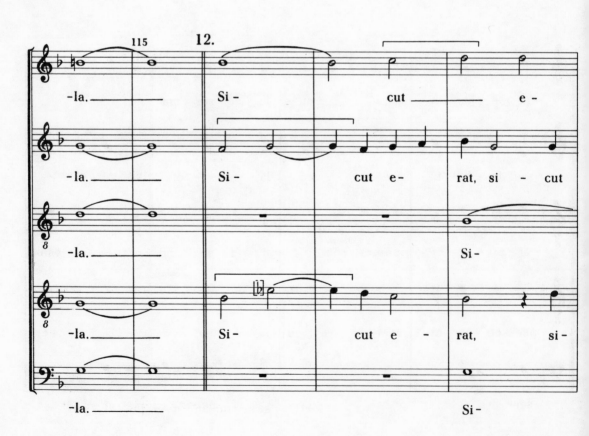

12.

-la. Si - cut e -

-la. Si - cut e- rat, si - cut

-la. Si-

-la. Si - cut e - rat, si-

-la. Si-

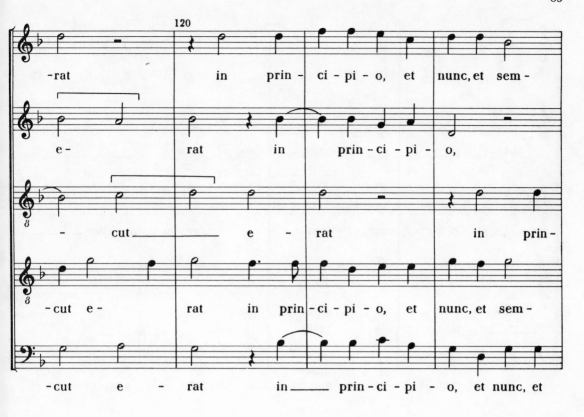

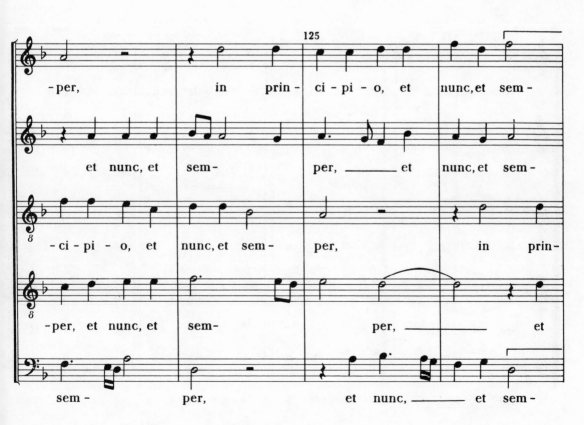

- per, et nunc, et ___ sem- per, et in

-per, et nunc, ___ et sem- -

-ci-pi-o, et nunc, et sem- per, et nunc, et ___

nunc, et sem- per,

- per, *et nunc,* ___ *et sem -* per, et nunc, et

sae- cu -la sae- cu -lo -rum, a - men,

- per, ___ et in sae -cu - la sae-

___ sem-per, et in sae- cu - la sae-

et in sae- cu - la sae - cu-

sem - per, et ___ in sae-cu - la sae- cu -lo -rum,

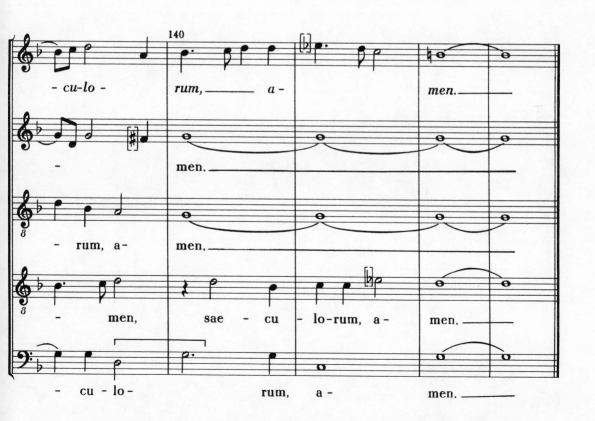

# Beatus vir
1576

# Beatus vir

## Tertij toni

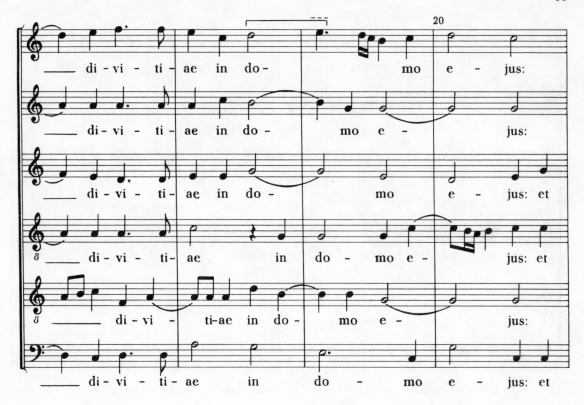

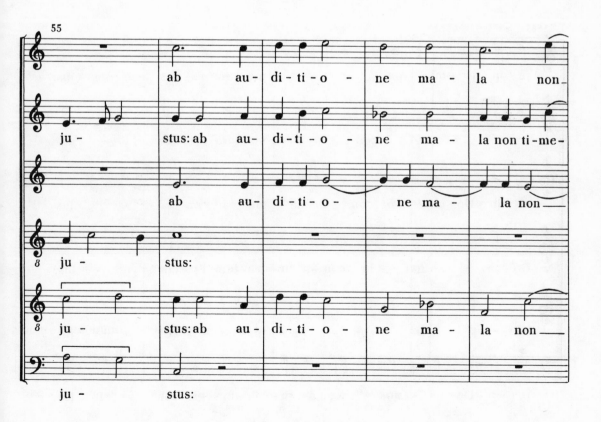

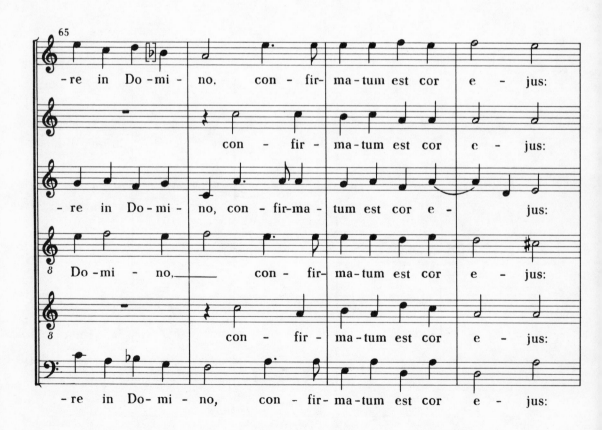

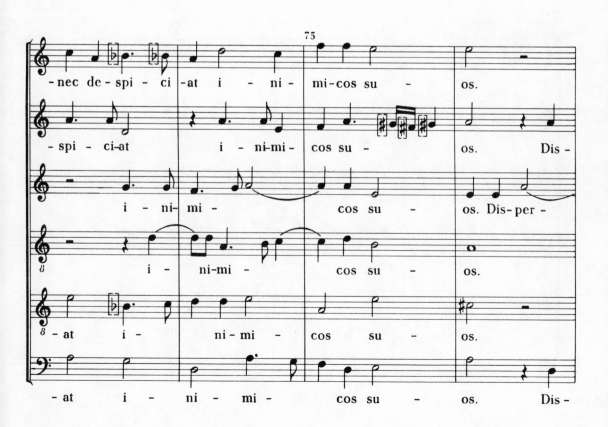

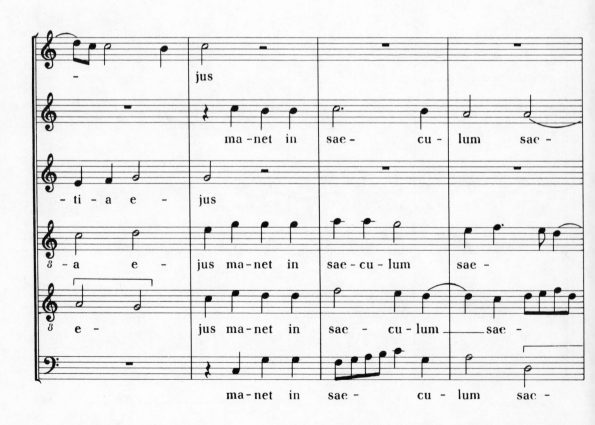

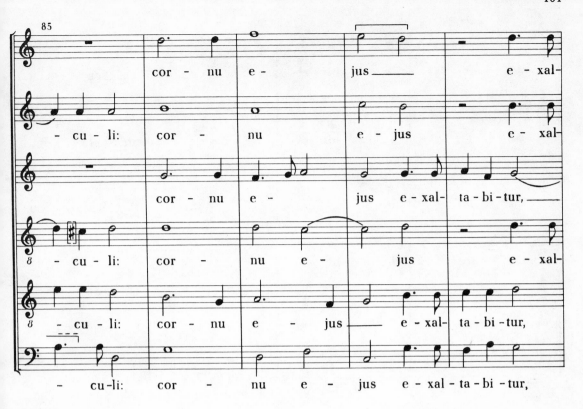

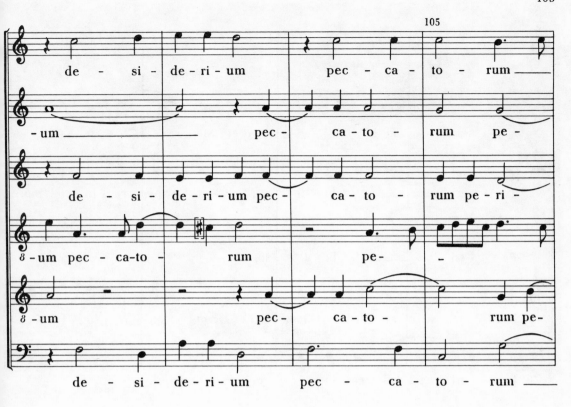

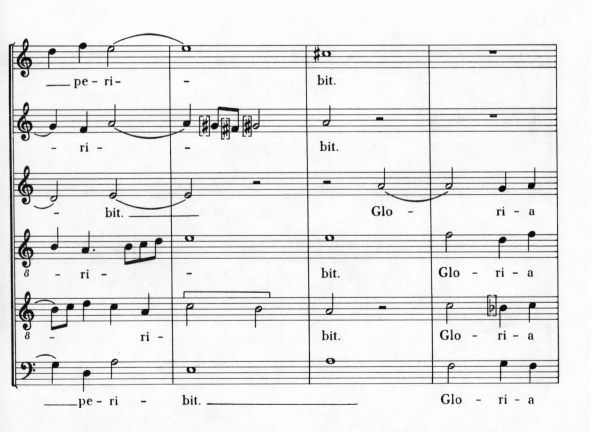

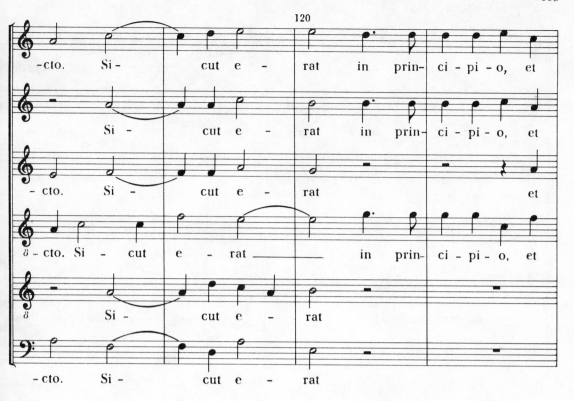

# Sacrae laudes
1588

# Deus canticum novum

## Cantate Domino